1909 - The interests of the Anglo-Persian Oil Company
(as The British Petroleum Company was originally called)
were confined to the operation of the D'Arcy concession, Persia

Fifty Years

in Pictures

A story in pictures of
the development of the
British Petroleum Group
1909-1959

Contents

Foreword

We have come a long way since that day in 1908 when oil spouted from Reynolds's rig at Masjid-i-Sulaiman. It has at times been a difficult and hilly road, but up to now every hill has had a summit which has been surmounted in the end.

This picture book does not attempt to present a factual history of these first 50 years. But we have tried to give an impression of some of the progress we have made and some of the milestones we have passed on the way.

Neville Gass.

CHAIRMAN

The seven-year search

The man who

began it all

William Knox D'Arcy, 1849-1917. A man of Devon, he had already made a fortune from gold mining in Australia when, at the turn of the century, he turned his attention to the legendary oil of Persia.

It was the turn of the century . . .

... when D'Arcy first started looking for oil in Persia

In 1901 D'Arcy was granted a 60 year concession by the Persian Government "to search for, obtain, exploit, develop, render suitable for trade, carry away and sell natural gas, petroleum, asphalt and ozokerite throughout the whole extent of the Persian Empire with the exception of the five Northern Provinces . . ."

The Asmari Mountain in South Persia. In this area oil was finally struck in commercial quantities.

as I much wanted to get things in train — Between ourselves Bad news came from Reynolds this week. It seems he has at last been able to get into the Country near Chardin (where he so often said he wished to go but could not with safety) and he there was able to ~~measure~~ measure the Bed of Gypsum the Drills are now going through

and he found this Gypsum bed measured 1500 yards and he has Recommended the shutting down of the two Bores at Chardin Hamilton & Redwood have not authorised this but have wired him to send a full Report and cease work in the meantime — He (Reynolds) further says he will commence Drilling at Masjid i Sulaiman Early in December there of course he will I am sure get oil but it is all most annoying

Bad news from Persia . . . but the first mention of Masjid-i-Sulaiman.

Seven years passed in the wilderness . . .

Between the start of D'Arcy's exploration and the striking of Persian oil in commercial quantities, seven agonising years passed – seven years of patience and impatience; of hopes raised and dashed; of hunches and dead ends; of thirst and dysentery; of heat stroke and inescapable sun.

Survey party takes the field.

One of the unsuccessful wells.

. . . before the finding of oil in Persia

On May 16th, 1908, drillers working at Masjid-i-Sulaiman in South Persia detected a "strong smell of petroleum gas" in the well. At 4 o'clock in the morning of May 26th oil was struck. The oil that was struck that day was something different from the oil that had been found from time to time during the seven struggling years of exploration. This, at last, was oil in commercial quantities. This, unquestionably, was the first fruits of a vast reservoir that lay waiting beneath the barren wilderness of Persia.

G. B. Reynolds, the man in charge at Masjid-i-Sulaiman, had long wanted to search for oil there. The first derricks had gone up in the West at Chia Surkh. Some oil was found – but not enough. When the Burmah Oil Company took over operations, forming a syndicate of which D'Arcy was one of the members, a move was made to the South. Once again, at Shardin, D'Arcy's men drew a blank. Then, at last, Reynolds took his team to Masjid-i-Sulaiman.

Oil gushes out at Masjid-i-Sulaiman.

G. B. Reynolds (left) in South Persia with
two of his colleagues, Willans and Crush.

Three of the men who found the first oil . . .

. . . and how the news came to London

In any further communica-
tion on this subject, please quote

No. 18570.

and address—
The Under-Secretary of State,
Foreign Office,
London.

FOREIGN OFFICE

June 3 . 1908.

Sir:-

I am directed by Secretary Sir Edward Grey to in-
form you that he has received a telegram from His Majesty's Chargé d'Affaires at Tehran reporting that the
operators of your Syndicate have struck oil at one thou-
sand two hundred feet which rises intermittently
seventy-five feet above the level of the ground.

Mr. Marling's telegram is founded on a telegraphic
report dated the 28th. ultimo from His Majesty's Consul
General at Bushire.

I am,

Sir,

Your most obedient,

humble Servant,

Louis Mallet

J. R. Preece, Esq., C.M.G.,
1, St. James' Place, S.W.

From beneath the mountains

of Persia the oil begins to flow

Masjid-i-Sulaiman in 1908: the camp and the workshop

While in Britain, in 1908, there were new customers for oil

A site for a refinery was chosen at Abadan

Masjid-i-Sulaiman's oil needed a refinery to make it usable. One of the first acts of the Anglo-Persian Oil Company, formed in April 1909 to take over the original D'Arcy concession, was to choose a refinery site. The site chosen was a barren mud flat on the Shatt-al-Arab river called Abadan.

By 1911, the first house was starting to take shape

Though most materials had to be brought across the sea, gradually there arose from the mud flat a modern town and the refinery which was to become the largest in the world.

Oilfield and refinery needed a link . . .

The mule trains hauling lengths of pipe began to trail across the South Persian plains. The men hacked and blasted hundreds of miles of road out of the hard rock of the Zagros mountains, so that the crude oil might start to flow through the pipeline laid from Masjid-i-Sulaiman to Abadan.

. . . and the men to forge the link

Legions of men had to be recruited – men to lay the pipeline, men for the oilfield and the refinery. Once recruited, the men had to be trained and taught the technique of a civilisation removed from their own. They had to be protected by modern medicine from the ancient banes of the desert – bad water, dysentery, flies. And, every week, they had to be paid.

Somewhere along the pipeline: Dr. M. Y. Young, medical officer of the Anglo-Persian Oil Company, with the British Consul at Ahwaz, Captain Grey, and his wife.

The first railway engine that the people of South Persia had ever seen was put into service on the Abadan building site in 1911.

The stern-wheeler "Dehluran" brings a party of Persian dignitaries on a visit.

The work of construction called for all kinds of transport

by road, rail and water

Every piece of heavy equipment, every tool, every screw, had to be brought
up to the oilfield, by mule and wagon, along treacherous mountain ledges.

Landing a boiler in 1914.

There was always . . .

... one more river to cross

Fording the Tembi river with equipment for the pumping station being built at Tembi.

The work of construction . . .

Some of the equipment looks
primitive but it worked.

The first boiler ever used at Masjid-
i-Sulaiman today stands monumentally
in front of No. 1 well.

... was hurried along to keep pace with the drilling

Examining the drilling bit of a Percussion Rig.

G. B. Scott, at the age of 65, sets out with his survey team in 1910.

A survey team.

The geologist's work was never done

Unceasingly, throughout these exploring years, the geologists and surveyors mapped, measured, surveyed – and marked the places where those who followed might tap the hidden oil for the use of man.

Map survey work near Masjid-i-Sulaiman.

The first market

is found for Persian oil

One day the young First Lord of the Admiralty made

a plan

Winston Churchill decided that this . . .

Oil seepage in South Persia.

... could be used to power this

One of the British Tanker Company's earliest ships.

Waterfront activity at the new Abadan Refinery.

The First Lord made the decision;

it was up to the Company to deliver the goods

In 1914 the Government invested money in the Company and, in the British Admiralty, the Anglo-Persian Oil Company had found its first major customer. The problem now was to get the oil from Abadan Refinery to the customer's dockyards in Britain. In 1915, the British Tanker Company was formed by the A.P.O.C. and a year later the first tanker built specially for the new company was launched - a ship of 5,500 deadweight tons. Seven more new tankers followed – into the war effort.

The 1914 War began with horses . . .

. . . but, half way through, the petrol engine arrived

The period of expansion

between the wars

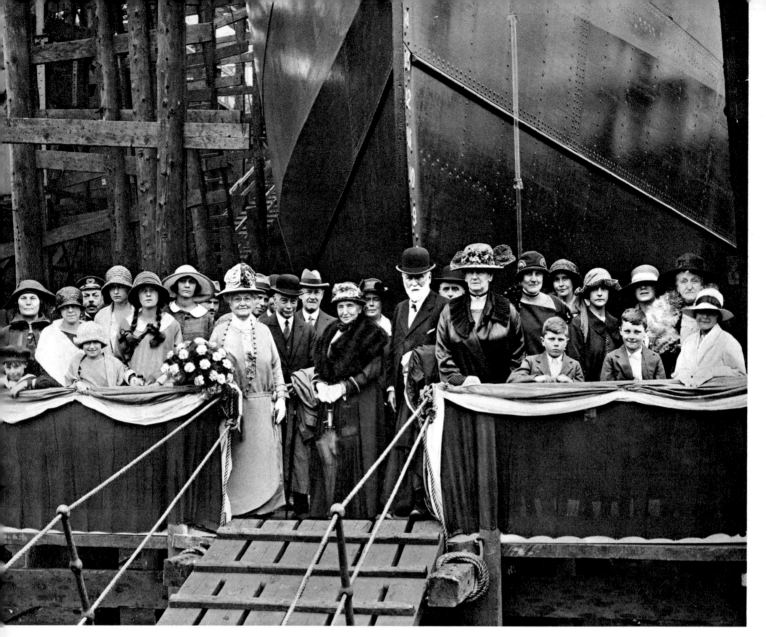

Launching of *British Motorist* at Wallsend-on-Tyne.

In peace, too, oil was ready to play its part

After the War the tanker fleet was promptly expanded

By 1924 a fleet of some 60 ships, totalling more than 500,000 tons, was afloat under the British Tanker Company's flag. The standard size built up to this time was 10,000 tons; but the Company now began to explore the advantages of building larger and faster ships.

British Aviator is launched at Jarrow-on-Tyne.

Llandarcy Refinery in its early days.

The tanker building went hand in hand with new refineries

Llandarcy Refinery, near Swansea, in South Wales, began to operate in 1921—the first large-scale refinery in the United Kingdom for the treatment of imported crude oil. Three years later, the Company's Grangemouth Refinery, on the Firth of Forth, began to operate.

The first major refinery in Britain was built at Llandarcy

Viscount Churchill, Lord
Cowdray and Mr. Andrew
Campbell, Managing Director
of the Refinery, test petrol
for quality by smell at the
opening of Llandarcy.

Workers leaving the refinery.

In Persia, Abadan became a centre of bustling life . . .

Abadan Refinery was enlarged. The number of workers was increased. Schools and hospitals were built and other social amenities were multiplied.

Drilling bit being treated in the blacksmith's shop at the oilfields.

Prince's Pier, Melbourne, in 1923: A.P.O.C. pipelines brought oil to the waiting ships.

. . . and passenger and cargo vessels were turning over to oil

A.P.O.C. barge delivers oil to the *City of Yokohama* at Colombo.

Captain J. C. Taylor on the Oxford University Arctic Expedition of 1924.

The Master of Sempill fuels his seaplane in front of the Houses of Parliament before his 1928 tour of Britain.

The Company's aviation service was founded

Fuelling the plane in which Captain Köhl, Baron von Huenefeld, and Major Fitzmaurice flew the Atlantic in 1928.

Early in the century, it had been the horses that
took the oil down to the quays and the beaches.

It had been the horse's job to deliver lamp oil.

But after 1918 the horse began to make way for the motor truck, in peace just as it had in war.

The petrol engine ceased to be a toy and the oil

industry was growing up

Drums of BP petrol being filled for despatch to Major H. O. D. Segrave for his successful attempt on the World Land Speed Record at Daytona Beach, Florida, in 1927.

The Hon. Mrs. Victor Bruce refuels during the 1928 Monte Carlo Rally.

The sale of petrol and oil spread

in Continental Europe and beyond

This standard 8-h.p. Singer covered 5,671 miles in 144 hours on the Montlhéry track, near Paris, in 1928.

An early type of kerbside filling point.

A mule loaded with cases of kerosine—a common method of transport in Persia and Iraq during the '20's.

On the race track, petrol broke new records every year

Between 1927 and 1937, the speeds recorded by motor racing drivers at Brooklands and other tracks in Britain, and on the Continent of Europe, brought home to the British public the spectacular possibilities of the petrol-driven engine.

The research unit's first home, Meadhurst, an old country house at Sunbury-on-Thames where Dr. A. E. Dunstan, one of the heads of the original unit, lived with his family and used the out-houses and cellars as laboratories.

All this progress owed much ...

Dr. Dunstan and Dr. F. B. Thole, two of the Company's research pioneers, in the original base-ment laboratory at Meadhurst.

A section of the main laboratory
at Sunbury in 1937.

. . . to the research that had been conducted by the Company

How the main research station at Sunbury
looked from the air in 1932.

Road building gang at work
near the Persian oilfields.

The struggle to find, and get, and

carry oil continued and was intensified

There were new drilling rigs to be
erected in the Zagros Mountains.

During the '30's more tankers brought

more and more oil to the European markets

The 12,000 ton tanker *British Endurance*, launched in 1936.

Steam wagon for bulk fuel in use before the formation of Shell-Mex and B.P. Limited.

A new company was formed in Britain

In 1932, during the depression, a move to improve economy in the distribution of products in the United Kingdom was made through the formation of Shell-Mex and B.P. Limited. The new Company was to carry out the activities in Britain previously performed by Shell-Mex Limited – the distributing organisation of the Shell and Eagle groups – and by the British Petroleum Company, which the A.P.O.C. had acquired in 1917 as a distributing organisation in the United Kingdom.

In the '30's the first major drillings for oil in Britain began

Inauguration of the Company's first British well, Portsdown No. 1, in 1936. Sir John (later Lord) Cadman, then Chairman of the Company, is second from left.

Portsdown No. 1 overlooked Portsmouth harbour.
The Company's first exploration success in Britain
came in 1939 with the discovery of the Eakring oilfield in Nottinghamshire.

At Baba Gurgur, near Kirkuk, on the morning
of 14th October, 1927, oil erupts high in the air.

In 1927, a gusher in Iraq opened up a whole new territory

The first pipeline, running from Kirkuk to the

Mediterranean, was completed in 1934

From the earliest days in Persia, the Anglo-Iranian Oil Company (as the A.P.O.C. became about this time) had been interested in the oil prospects of the neighbouring Turkish territory which, after the First World War, became Iraq. The Company was a shareholder in the Turkish Petroleum Company which discovered the Kirkuk field in 1927; and it had a $23\frac{3}{4}$ per cent interest in its successor, the Iraq Petroleum Company.

Digging the trench for the Kirkuk-Mediterranean pipeline.

Kuwaiti rig men running a drill pipe.

Another area which attracted the Company's attention

was the Sheikhdom of Kuwait

In 1934 the Kuwait Oil Company was formed as a joint undertaking of the
A.I.O.C. and the Gulf Oil Corporation of the United States. Four years
later Kuwait's great Burgan oilfield was discovered.

Long before its oil
was discovered, Kuwait
was famous for the
dhows it built.

Britain goes to war

September 1939: digging A.R.P. trenches in St. James's Park, London.

The second

world war is fought on oil

At the outbreak of war the Anglo-Iranian Oil Company's

tanker fleet numbered 93 ocean-going tankers

Nearly half these ships and 657 men were lost by enemy action

The Dunkirk Refinery goes up in flames, 1940.

In England, rail tank cars were bombed.

The Special Products Area for the production of aviation spirit at Abadan Refinery.

But the enemy were effectively denied the great

oil producing areas of the Middle East

Crusader tanks moving up to the battle area.

One of the huge bobbins that unwound
" Pluto "—the oil pipeline under the
ocean which supplied the liberating
armies from Normandy to Berlin.

On every front . . .

Lancaster bomber over the target.

... the war was fought and won on oil

Post-war Europe looks to the

Middle East for its oil supplies

Building a new power house at Abadan Refinery.

A world at peace

It was to the Middle East that the Allies had looked during the war. It was to the Middle East that a world at peace looked once more. And the Middle East responded with great expansions in the production and refining of oil.

Drilling a new
well in Kuwait.

De-gassing station in
the Kirkuk oilfield.

Peace brought new pipelines over the Persian mountains . . .

The oil well fire at Naft Safid.

. . . and it brought its own kind of hazards into the oilmen's lives

The great plant left behind . . .

... by the Britons who evacuated Abadan in 1951

In 1949, the Iranian Government and the Company had negotiated a supplemental agreement, which gave the Iranian nation additional benefits from the oil industry. But nationalisation of the oil industry was becoming a political issue. The Iranian Parliament declined to ratify the agreement, and after Dr. Mosaddeq took power the Company, having made every possible effort at negotiation, was left with no alternative but to shut down its operations and evacuate its personnel.

Refineries

increase and multiply

After the loss of Abadan, new refineries were

built and old ones enlarged and modernised

A surge of activity carried the Company through this difficult period. At the
end of 1954 the Company changed its name to The British Petroleum Company.

Queen Elizabeth, the Queen Mother, with the Company's then Chairman, Sir William Fraser (now Lord Strathalmond) on a visit to Grangemouth Refinery, already well ahead with its programme of expansion.

The majestic column of No. 1 Distillation Unit rose above
the marshes of Kent as the new Kent Refinery took shape
on the Isle of Grain.

At Llandarcy Refinery: the cathedral-like interior of the
base of a water cooling tower.

The Antwerp Refinery, which is owned jointly by BP and the Belgian company, Petrofina, was officially opened in 1952. To-day it has a processing capacity of 4,000,000 tons of crude oil a year.

A new refinery

at Antwerp . .

Control room of the catalytic reformer at Porto Marghera Refinery, near Venice, which is jointly owned by BP and the Italian organisation, AGIP.

. . . at Kuwait and Hamburg

His Highness the Ruler of Kuwait arrives for the inauguration of the enlarged Mina al Ahmadi Refinery.

Hamburg Refinery from the air.

At Dunkirk Refinery.

Refineries in the Middle East . . .

At Aden a new refinery arose from the sands in under two years.

. . . Europe and Canada

Work began on a new refinery in Canada, at Montreal . . . and on another in the Ruhr, Germany.

Interior of oil storage tank at Lavera Refinery, near Marseilles.

The official opening, by the Governor-General, Sir
William Slim, of the Kwinana Refinery, Western
Australia, in 1955.

A new refinery in Australia

Distant view of oil and chemical installations at Grangemouth.

Refineries in Britain . . .

BP's Grangemouth Refinery, on the Firth of Forth, has been greatly expanded and now has a processing capacity of 3,200,000 tons a year. Three BP associates manufacturing petroleum chemicals have plants adjoining the refinery, from which the initial feedstock is drawn. Grangemouth receives its crude oil through a 57-mile pipeline across Scotland from a deep water tanker terminal at Finnart on Loch Long.

Section of Finnart-Grangemouth pipeline before it was trenched.

Night scene at BP's Kent Refinery, on the Isle of Grain,
which can process 7,200,000 tons of crude oil a year.

The oil explorers

spread out across the world

As well as refinery expansion the long search

for new oilfields was intensified

Helicopter negotiating an outcrop of rock during a geological survey by Triad Oil Co. (in which BP has approximately a 50 per cent interest) at Jasper National Park, Western Alberta, Canada.

The snows of Canada mean horses for the surveyors.

Exploration . . .

The marshes of Basrah mean that seismic survey parties of the Basrah Petroleum Company must use amphibious vehicles known as marsh-buggies.

. . . all over the world

The Tanganyika bush closes in
on a survey party.

In the steaming rain forest of
Papua the oil men continue their
long search.

The land surfaces were examined

In the shadow of the cathedral of the walled city of Mdina in Malta, a surveyor of the BP Exploration Company takes an instrument reading.

Before BP could start work in Libya, wartime minefields laid by both sides had to be cleared.

Geologists examining the rock structure during a survey in New Zealand.

A student surveyor goes to work in Nigeria, where BP is jointly interested with the Royal Dutch/Shell group in oil exploration. Test production and export from Nigerian oilfields began in 1958.

Sunset view of Umm Shaif No. 1 We[ll] being drilled in the Persian Gulf.

Drilling six miles off the coast of Trinidad.

There was exploration, too, offshore and under the sea

Diver taking sample of rock from the sea-bed in preparation for drilling in the Persian Gulf.

Firing a charge during a seismic survey in Zanzibar.

The echoes of the seismic survey parties

activities were heard far and wide

Operating seismic recording equipment in Kuwait.

Seismic explosion in England.

A pump man watches the motion of his unit at Eakring oilfield, Nottinghamshire.

Work went on in all sorts of climates and conditions

Helicopter about to take off from a landing platform in a forest clearing in Papua.

Bulldozer makes a new road in Canada by laying a log mattress across a swampy patch.

A huge mechanical shovel goes to work at road building for the Iraq Petroleum Company.

Transport

and marketing

Giant new tankers were built and launched to carry

the ever-growing quantities of oil

The 28,000 ton *British Realm*.

Her Majesty The Queen with Captain H. I. McMichael
inspecting the 32,000 ton tanker *British Sailor*.

H.R.H. Princess Alexandra of Kent launches
the 32,000 ton *British Soldier* in 1954.

Another BP tanker of 32,000
ons being built at Belfast.

First of BP's 42,000 ton tankers, *British Duchess*, slides down the slipway after her launching on the Clyde by H.R.H. The Duchess of Gloucester in 1958. The 42,000 tonners are being followed by tankers of 50,000 and 65,000 tons.

. . . and still more tankers

British Duchess at speed during her trials.

Refinery area and South Pier, Mina al Ahmadi, Kuwait.

One of the sights that tanker men know well: Kuwait

Pipeway on oil pier, Mina al Ahmadi.

On land transport vehicles are being streamlined . . .

"Mastodon" road tanker in Norway.

. . and growing bigger

Transport by rail and sea . . .

. . . by road and rive

Delivering gas oil by caique
in the Greek Islands.

BP rail tank cars on
viaduct in Switzerlan

Giant road tanker of BP Australia on the New South Wales coast.

BP barge on the River Seine.

Austria.

New kinds of service stations are making their appearance . .

England.

Switzerland.

... in all parts of the world

North Africa

Canada.

137

Night fuelling at Orly Airport, Paris.

Hydrant fuelling at Daka

Refuelling helicopter, Bromma Airport, Stockholm.

The aviation service is being extended . . .

The BP aviation service was renamed Air BP on 1st
January, 1959: a fueller in the new colours at Amsterdam.

The BP International Oil Bunkering
Service in action at Dunkirk. This service today covers more than 190 ports.

. . . and bunkering installations are being modernised

The bunkering installation at Trieste.
Today some 92 per cent of the world's
ships run on oil.

The challenge

of the future

The future depends on research

Testing aviation gas turbine fuels
at Sunbury Research Centre.

Measuring the viscosity of lubricating oil. This is the property which determines the oil's rate of flow.

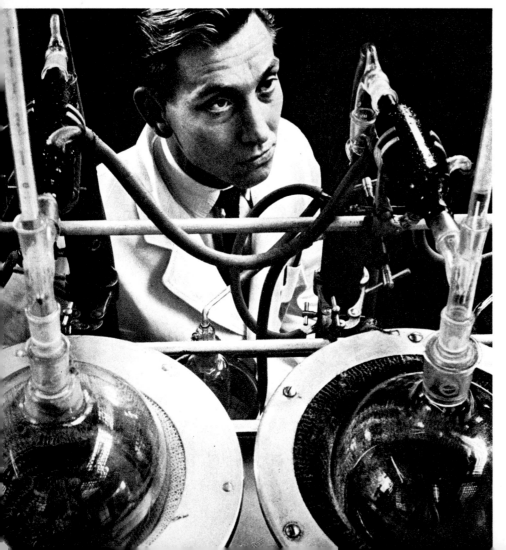

Carrying out a test on petrols of the future.

Every year BP's geologists send thousands of rock fragments from all over the world to the Palaeontological Laboratory at Sunbury, where the samples are examined to assess the oil-bearing possibilities of the areas being surveyed.

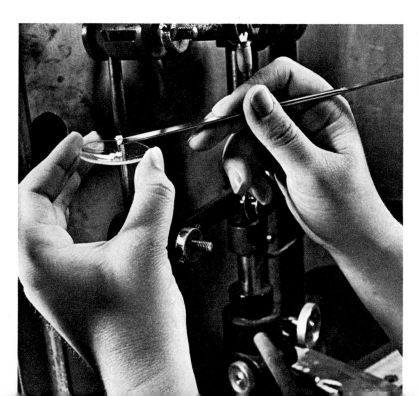

A sample of catalyst about to be analysed in a spectrometer. This type of material is used in catalytic cracking plants for the production of high quality petrols.

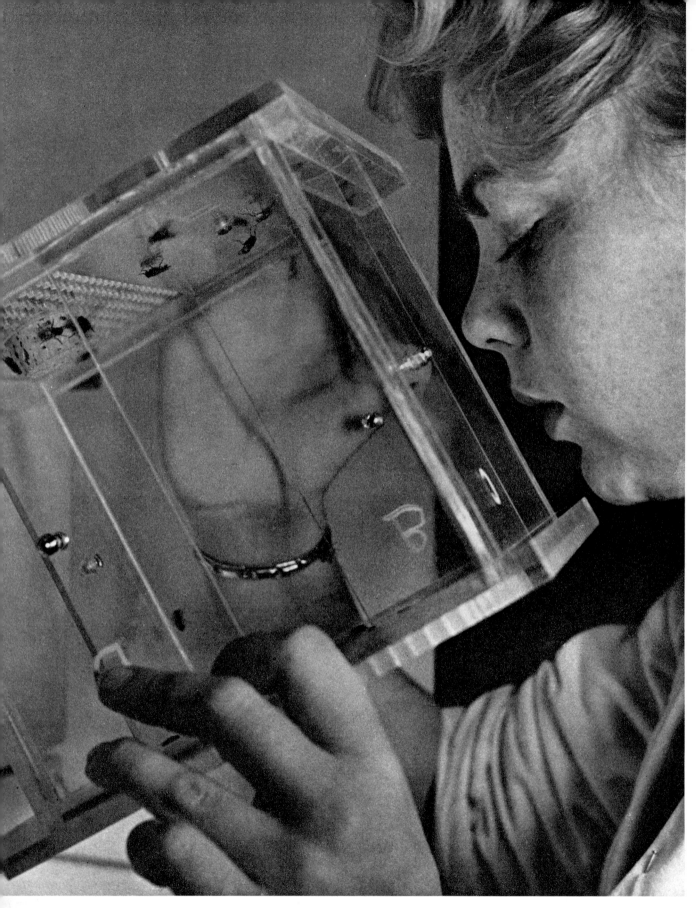

A research assistant in the Insecticide
Laboratory makes an insect repellency test.

Aerial view of BP's Sunbury Research Centre.

The future depends on new ships . . .

Welding in progress during the construction of a new 50,000 ton tanker for BP on the Clyde.

... and on new installations

British Hydrocarbon Chemicals plant at Grangemouth. BP has a 50 per cent interest in BHC.

BP's deep water tanker terminal on Milford Haven under
construction, with an old fort being converted into offices.

The future depends on people

154

Some of the BP family

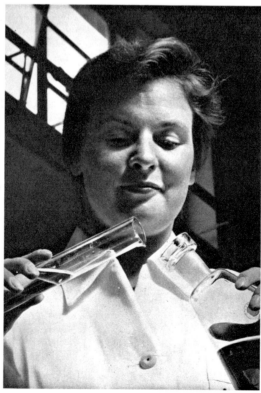

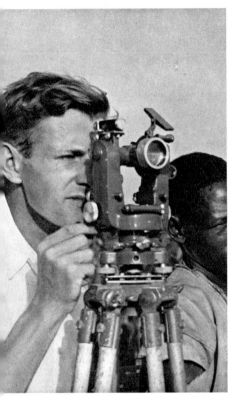

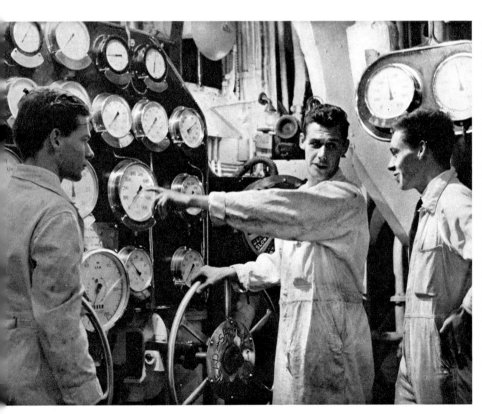

THE BRITISH PETROLEUM COMPANY LIMITED is the parent company of the BP Group, one of the major international petroleum organisations engaged in all phases of the industry, including exploration, production, transportation, refining, research and marketing in many parts of the world.

Its principal sources of crude oil are in the Middle East and through its prospecting subsidiary, the BP Exploration Company, it also has oil production or exploration interests in many other parts of the world, including Great Britain where it has producing oilfields in the Midlands.

The BP Group operates refineries in Great Britain, Australia, Aden, France, Germany, Belgium, Italy and the Middle East. In association with chemical producers, it has growing interests in the petroleum chemical field in the United Kingdom, France and Germany. Its marketing network extends over much of the eastern hemisphere and also includes Canada.

For sea transport, the Group has interests in a number of shipping companies, one of which, the wholly owned BP Tanker Company, operates one of the largest fleets in the world.

The Group's research organisation is based on its principal Research Station at Sunbury-on-Thames, Middlesex.

The BP shield is the symbol of the world-wide organisation of

THE BRITISH PETROLEUM GROUP

Designed and produced by Contact Publications Limited for
The British Petroleum Company Limited, Britannic House, Finsbury Circus, London, E.C.2
Printed in Great Britain by Clarke and Sherwell Ltd., Northampton